HOW TO TAKE CARE OF YOUR PET
DINOSAUR

YOUR PET
STEGOSAURUS

By Kirsty Holmes

THE
OFFICIAL
F.O.S.S.I.L
GUIDE

THE SECRET BOOK COMPANY

©2019
The Secret Book Company
King's Lynn
Norfolk PE30 4LS

ISBN: 978-1-912502-44-8

All rights reserved

Printed in Malaysia

A catalogue record for this book is available from the British Library.

Written by:
Kirsty Holmes

Edited by:
Madeline Tyler

Designed by:
Danielle Jones

All facts, statistics, web addresses and URLs in this book were verified as valid and accurate at time of writing. No responsibility for any changes to external websites or references can be accepted by either the author or publisher.

IMAGE CREDITS

CONTENTS

THE OFFICIAL F.O.S.S.I.L GUIDE

Words that look like this can be found in the glossary on page 24.

F.O.S.S.I.L

So, you're the proud owner of a dinosaur egg. Congratulations!

Owning a pet dinosaur is a lot of hard work, but it's worth the trouble. Dinosaurs make excellent pets.

Per 1
Gn +1
C6/M7
P5/E2
M1 1.3

CONGRATULATIONS! IT'S A... STEGOSAURUS!

If you are a first-time dinosaur owner, you probably have lots of questions. Never fear! This handy F.O.S.S.I.L guide will tell you all you need to know.

F.O.S.S.I.L
FACT

F.O.S.S.I.L stands for:

Federal
Office of
Super
Sized
Interesting
Lizards

HOW TO TAKE CARE OF YOUR PET
DINOSAUR
YOUR PET
STEGOSAURUS
THE OFFICIAL F.O.S.S.I.L GUIDE

EGGS

Stegosaurus eggs are <u>spherical</u>. They are about 11 centimetres (cm) wide.

11 CM

Stegosaurus eggs should be kept in a <u>shallow</u> <u>nest</u>, dug into some sand.

YOUR EGG WILL DO WELL IF KEPT WARM, SO BUILD YOUR NEST IN A SUNNY PLACE.

BABIES

When it <u>hatches</u>, your Stegosaurus will be around the size of a kitten. Keep your pet in a closed, quiet room at first. They will be quite shy.

YOUR PET WILL NEED SOME TOYS AND A LITTER TRAY.

Feed your Stegosaurus <u>mosses</u> and ferns. Stegosaurus doesn't have a strong bite, so go ahead and feed your pet from your hands.

GROWTH

Your Stegosaurus will grow slowly and steadily. Babies are around the size of cats. Teenagers are around 5.6 metres (m) long, and 2.5 m tall.

TEEN

BABY

Adults can grow as long as 9 m and weigh up to 7 tonnes. This is very heavy, so it might not be a good idea to let your Stegosaurus live upstairs.

ADULT

FOOD

Stegosaurs are herbivores, which means they only eat plants. They have small teeth and a weak bite.

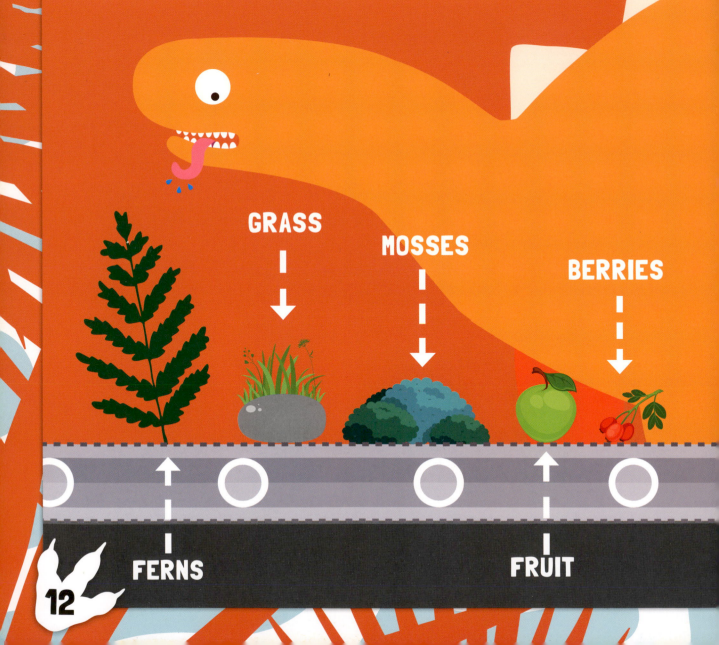

GRASS

MOSSES

BERRIES

FERNS

FRUIT

Because its teeth are so small, your Stegosaurus might eat small stones. These are called gastroliths and roll aroundin the stomach to help the Stegosaurus <u>digest</u> its food.

EXERCISE

Your Stegosaurus won't need much exercise. They walk very slowly and spend most of the day eating. Try a gentle walk around the park if your pet is in the mood.

Stegosaurus has long spikes on the end of its tail. It is safest to stay at the front of your pet when going for walks to avoid being hit.

F.O.S.S.I.L FACT

Your Stegosaurus will walk slowly but is very heavy. Don't let them tread on your toes.

NAMING

Naming your Stegosaurus is very important when <u>bonding</u> with your pet. You could choose to use the first letter, S, when choosing a name.

SOPHIE

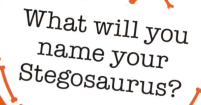

F.O.S.S.I.L FACT

What will you name your Stegosaurus?

You could use words that describe your Stegosaurus to name it instead. Stegosaurus has huge <u>armoured</u> plates and a spiky tail.

SPIKE!

WASHING

It is important that you keep your pet clean, especially between its plates. You will need:

POLISH

GOGGLES

SCRUBBING BRUSH

A LADDER

WELLIES

A CLOTH

A BUCKET

Make sure to carefully polish the plates to a nice shine.
This will bring out the colours.

PROBLEMS

Stegosaurus has a small brain – only about as big as a walnut. This means they aren't very bright and can easily get into trouble.

WE RECOMMEND KEEPING A CLOSE EYE ON YOUR PET.

One problem with herbivores is that they make a lot of…
well… gas. That's another good reason to stay at the head
end of your pet at all times.

GROSS!

TRICKS

As your Stegosaurus won't be very bright, it won't learn tricks easily. However, you can try climbing onto its back using its armoured plates.

ROLL OVER!

THERE ARE HOURS OF FUN TO BE HAD WITH YOUR FRIENDLY NEW PET!

Stegosaurus will love to learn a few simple commands. If you can be patient, it is very rewarding.

GLOSSARY

ARMOURED   strong, covered in armour

BONDING   forming a close relationship

DIGEST   break down food into things that can be used by the body

HATCHES   when a baby animal comes out of its egg

MOSSES   small flowerless plants which grow in clumps

NEST   any place used by an animal to lay eggs or rear young

SHALLOW   not deep

SPHERICAL   the shape of a ball

INDEX